ive Distributors:
Sales Limited
th Street,
n W1V 5TZ, England.
Sales Pty Limited
othschild Avenue,
ery, NSW 2018,
lia.

No. AM950246
-7119-7007-6
ook © Copyright 1997 by Wise Publications

Publications
n/New York/Paris/Sydney/Copenhagen/Madrid

GUITAR TABLATURE EXPLAINED

Guitar music can be notated three different ways: on a musical stave, in tablature, and in rhythm slashes

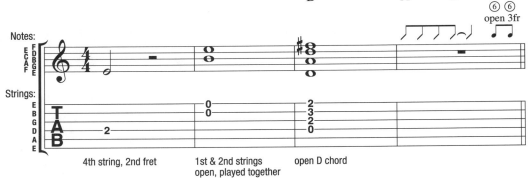

RHYTHM SLASHES are written above the stave. Strum chords in the rhythm indicated. Round noteheads indicate single notes.

THE MUSICAL STAVE shows pitches and rhythms and is divided by lines into bars. Pitches are named after the first seven letters of the alphabet.

TABLATURE graphically represents the guitar fingerboard. Each horizontal line represents a string, and each number represents a fret.

4th string, 2nd fret   1st & 2nd strings open, played together   open D chord

DEFINITIONS FOR SPECIAL GUITAR NOTATION

SEMI-TONE BEND: Strike the note and bend up a semi-tone (1/2 step).

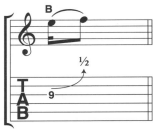

WHOLE-TONE BEND: Strike the note and bend up a whole-tone (whole step).

GRACE NOTE BEND: Strike the note and bend as indicated. Play the first note as quickly as possible.

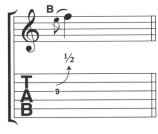

QUARTER-TONE BEND: Strike the note and bend up a 1/4 step.

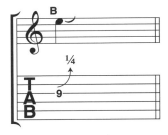

BEND & RELEASE: Strike the note and bend up as indicated, then release back to the original note.

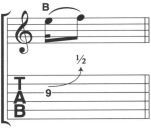

COMPOUND BEND & RELEASE: Strike the note and bend up and down in the rhythm indicated.

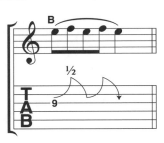

PRE-BEND: Bend the note as indicated, then strike it.

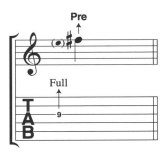

PRE-BEND & RELEASE: Bend the note as indicated. Strike it and release the note back to the original pitch.

UNISON BEND: Strike the two notes simultaneously and bend the lower note up to the pitch of the higher.

BEND & RESTRIKE: Strike the note and bend as indicated then restrike the string where the symbol occurs.

BEND, HOLD AND RELEASE: Same as bend and release but hold the bend for the duration of the tie.

BEND AND TAP: Bend the note as indicated and tap the higher fret while still holding the bend.

VIBRATO: The string is vibrated by rapidly bending and releasing the note with the fretting hand.

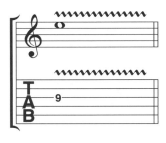

HAMMER-ON: Strike the first (lower) note with one finger, then sound the higher note (on the same string) with another finger by fretting it without picking.

PULL-OFF: Place both fingers on the notes to be sounded, Strike the first note and without picking, pull the finger off to sound the second (lower) note.

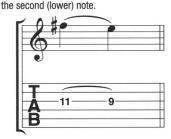

LEGATO SLIDE (GLISS): Strike the first note and then slide the same fret-hand finger up or down to the second note. The second note is not struck.

NOTE: The speed of any bend is indicated by the music notation and tempo.

SHIFT SLIDE (GLISS & RESTRIKE): Same as legato slide, except the second note is struck.

TRILL: Very rapidly alternate between the notes indicated by continuously hammering on and pulling off.

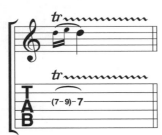

TAPPING: Hammer ("tap") the fret indicated with the pick-hand index or middle finger and pull off to the note fretted by the fret hand.

PICK SCRAPE: The edge of the pick is rubbed down (or up) the string, producing a scratchy sound.

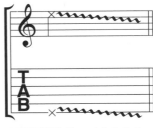

MUFFLED STRINGS: A percussive sound is produced by laying the fret hand across the string(s) without depressing, and striking them with the pick hand.

NATURAL HARMONIC: Strike the note while the fret-hand lightly touches the string directly over the fret indicated.

PINCH HARMONIC: The note is fretted normally and a harmonic is produced by adding the edge of the thumb or the tip of the index finger of the pick hand to the normal pick attack.

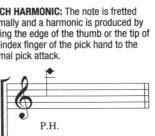

HARP HARMONIC: The note is fretted normally and a harmonic is produced by gently resting the pick hand's index finger directly above the indicated fret (in parentheses) while the pick hand's thumb or pick assists by plucking the appropriate string.

PALM MUTING: The note is partially muted by the pick hand lightly touching the string(s) just before the bridge.

RAKE: Drag the pick across the strings indicated with a single motion.

TREMOLO PICKING: The note is picked as rapidly and continuously as possible.

ARPEGGIATE: Play the notes of the chord indicated by quickly rolling them from bottom to top.

SWEEP PICKING: Rhythmic downstroke and/or upstroke motion across the strings.

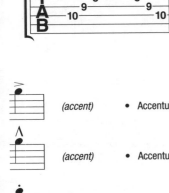

VIBRATO DIVE BAR AND RETURN: The pitch of the note or chord is dropped a specific number of steps (in rhythm) then returned to the original pitch.

VIBRATO BAR SCOOP: Depress the bar just before striking the note, then quickly release the bar.

VIBRATO BAR DIP: Strike the note and then immediately drop a specific number of steps, then release back to the original pitch.

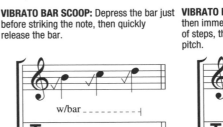

ADDITIONAL MUSICAL DEFINITIONS

> (accent)	•	Accentuate note (play it louder).
∧ (accent)	•	Accentuate note with great intensity.
• (staccato)	•	Shorten time value of note.
⊓	•	Downstroke
V	•	Upstroke

D.%. al Coda

• Go back to the sign (%), then play until the bar marked ***To Coda*** ⊕ then skip to the section marked ⊕ ***Coda***.

D.C. al Fine

• Go back to the beginning of the song and play until the bar marked ***Fine*** (end).

tacet

• Instrument is silent (drops out).

• Repeat bars between signs.

1.	2.

• When a repeated section has different endings, play the first ending only the first time and the second ending only the second time.

NOTE: Tablature numbers in parentheses mean: 1. The note is sustained, but a new articulation (such as hammer on or slide) begins.
2. A note may be fretted but not necessarily played.

ABSOLUTE BEGINNERS

Words & Music by Paul Weller

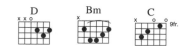

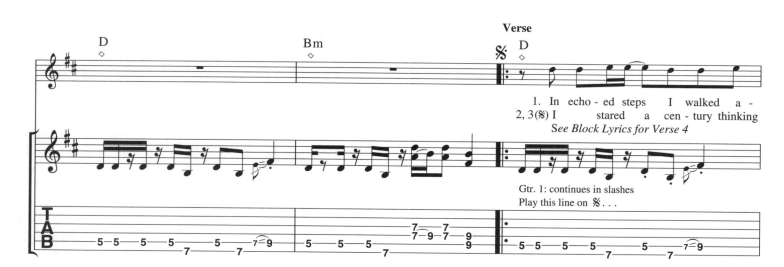

- cross an emp - ty dream, I looked a - cross this world there's
this will nev - er change, as I hes - i - tat - ed time rushed

no - one to be seen. This emp - ty feel - ing turned and quiet - ly walked a - way,
on - wards with - out me. Too scared to break the spell, too small to take a fall,

I saw no warmth in life and no love was in my eyes.
but the ab - so - lute luck is love is in our hearts.

1, 3.

2, 4.

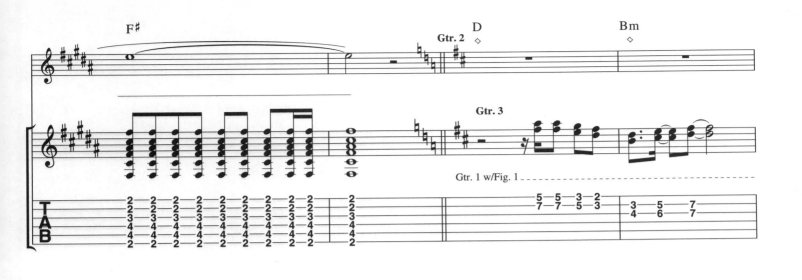

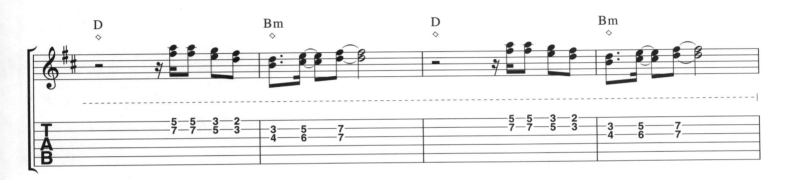

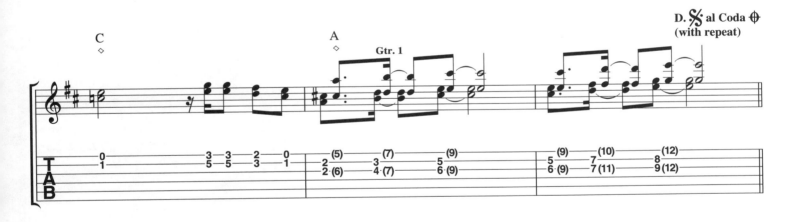

And lost an er - a day - dream - ing like I do.

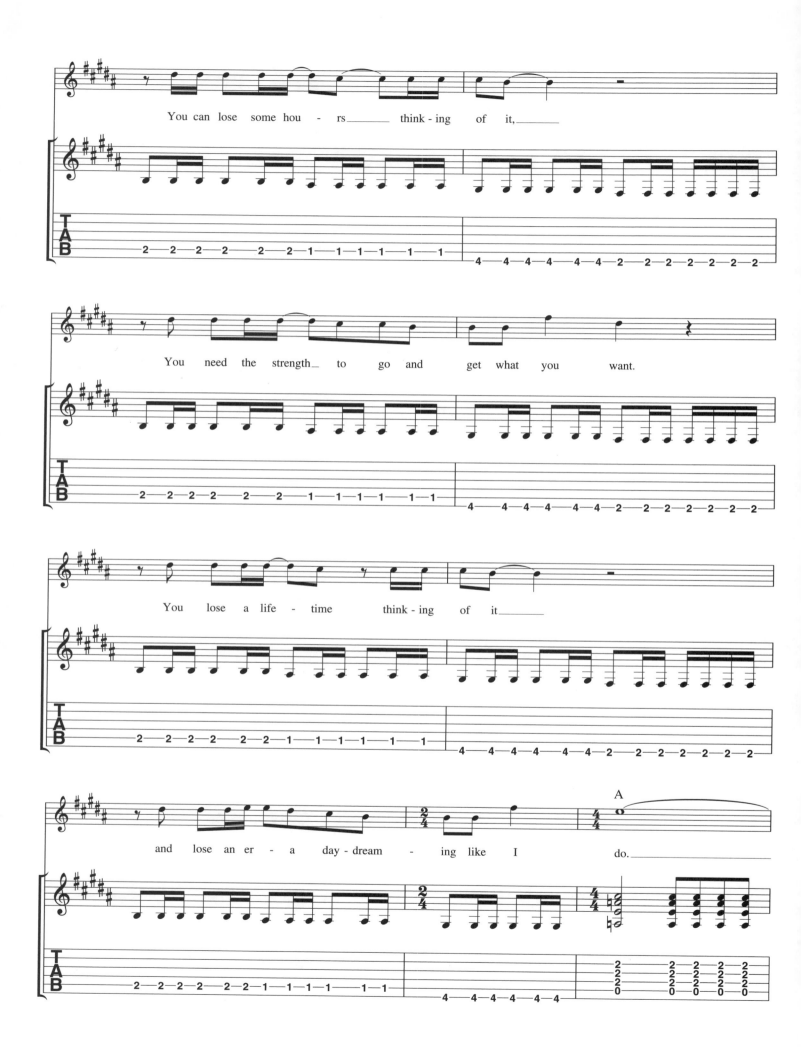

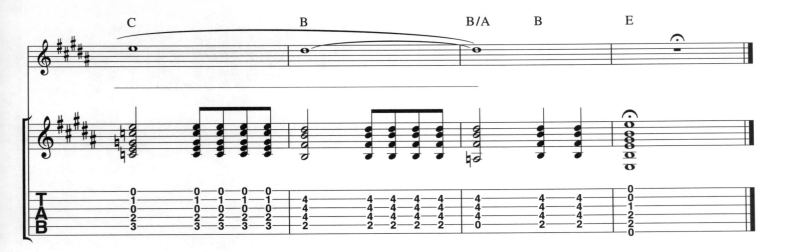

Verse 4:   In echoed steps you walk across an empty dream
But look around this world, there's millions to be seen
Come see the tyrants panic
See their crumbling empires fall
Then tell them we don't fight for fools
'Cause love is in our hearts!

ALL AROUND THE WORLD

Words & Music by Paul Weller

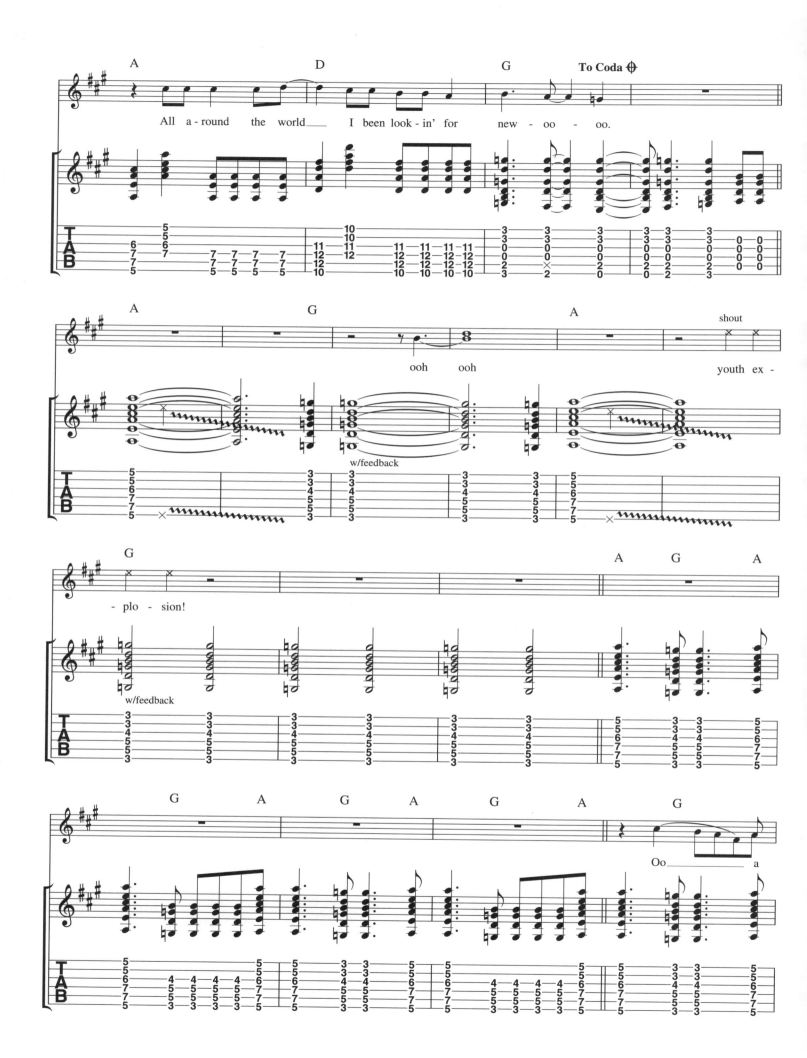

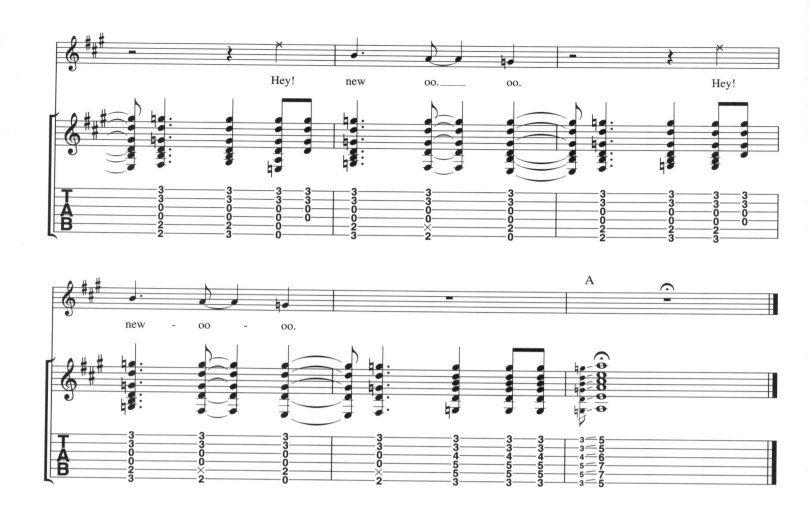

Verse 2:

We want a direction
(All over the country)
I said I want a reaction
(All over this land)
You gotta get up and be there
(A youth explosion)
Because this is your last chance.

Bridge:

You can't dismiss what is gone before
But there's foundations for us to explore

BITTEREST PILL

Words & Music by Paul Weller

ETON RIFLES

Words & Music by Paul Weller

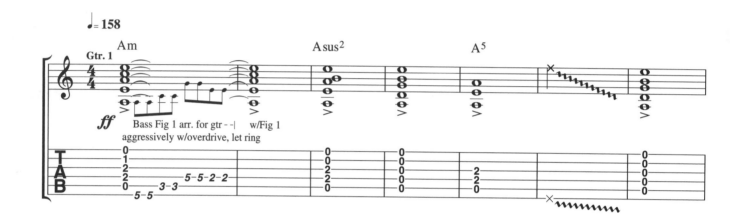

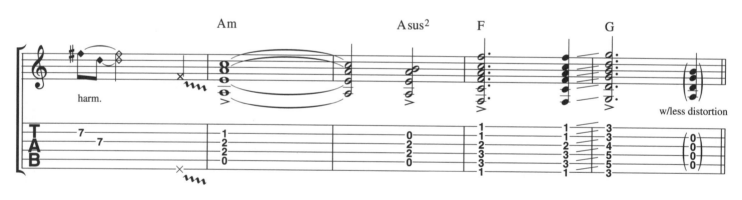

1. Sup up your beer and col-lect your fags,___ there's a row go-ing on
2. Thought you were smart when you took them on___ but you did-n't take a peep in their ar-
See Block Lyrics for Verses 3 & 4 (℅)

down near Slough.
-till - er - y room.
Get out your mat and pray___ to the west,___
All that rug - by puts hairs___ on your chest,___ what

I'll get out mine and pray___ for my - self.___
chance have you got a - gainst a tie and a crest.

Chorus

1.2. Hel - lo hur - ray,
See block lyrics for Chorus 3
what a nice day for the

E - ton Ri - fles, E - ton Ri - fles. Hel - lo hur - ray, I hope rain stops play with the

E - ton ri - fles, E - ton ri - fles.

What a cat-a-lyst you turned out to be, load-ed your guns then you ran off home__ for your tea,__ Left me stand-ing like a guilt-y school-boy.__

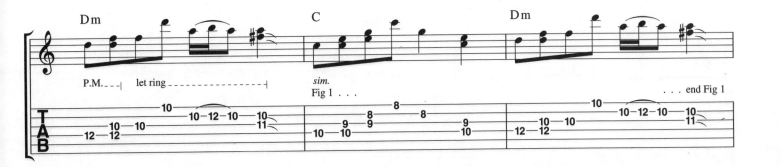

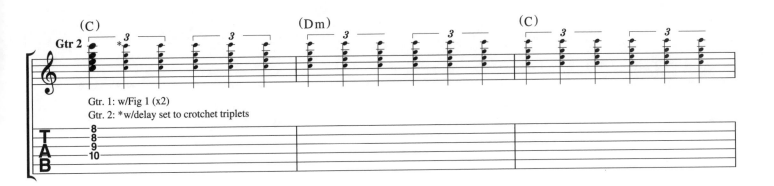

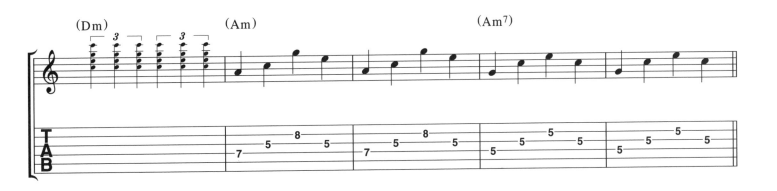

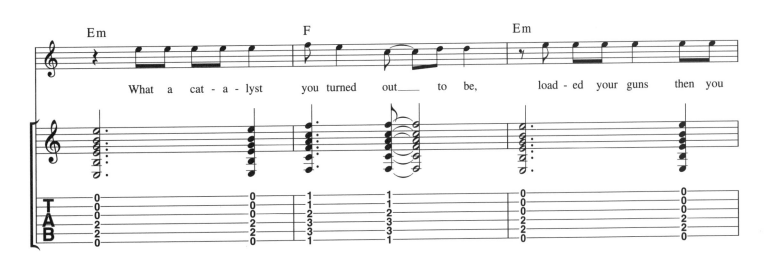

What a cat-a-lyst you turned out____ to be, load-ed your guns then you

24

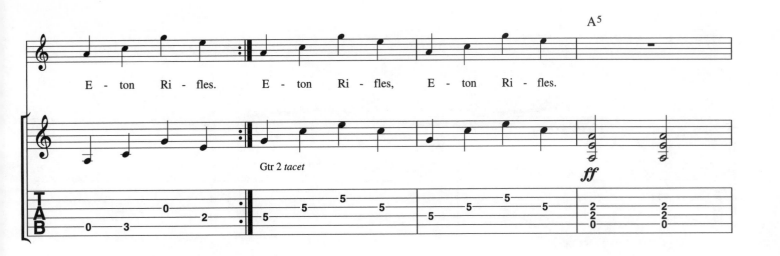

E - ton Ri - fles. E - ton Ri - fles, E - ton Ri - fles.

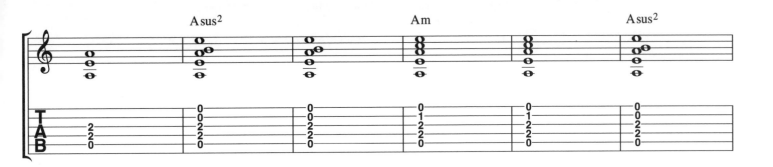

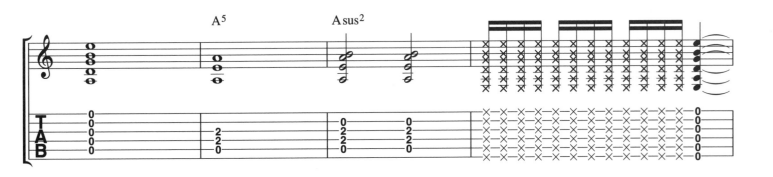

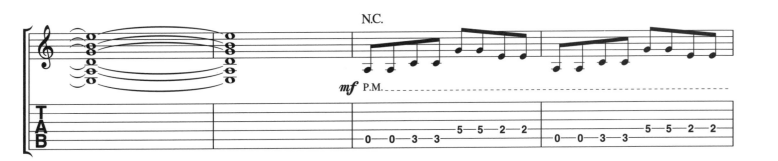

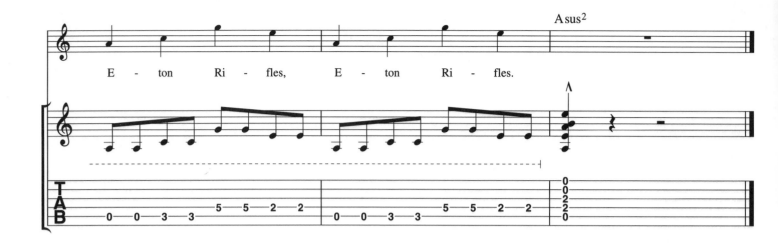

Verse 3:   Thought you were clever when you lit the fuse
                          Tore down the House of Commons in your brand new shoes
                          Compose a revolutionary symphony
                          Then went to bed with a charming young thing.

Chorus 3:   Hello hurray, cheers then mate, it's the Eton Rifles
                          Hello hurray, an extremist scrape, with the Eton Rifles.

Verse 4(%)   We came out of it naturally the worst
                          Beaten and bloody and I was sick down my shirt
                          We were no match for their untamed wit
                          Though some of the lads said they'd be back next week.

FUNERAL PYRE

Words & Music by Paul Weller, Bruce Foxton & Rick Buckler

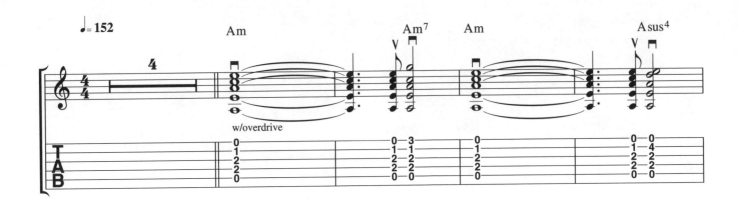

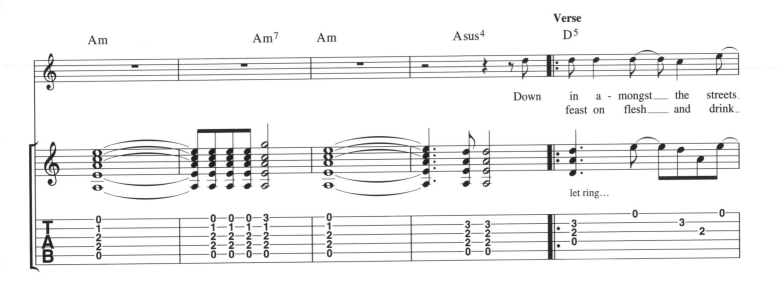

Am

moil___ (tur - moil turns re - joice - ful.)
- sis___ (what with to-day's high pri - ces.)

Chord implying gtr. & bass

D⁵

Shed your fears___ and lose___ your guilt,___ to - night we burn___ res - pon - si -
Bring some pa - per and bring some ___ wood, bring what's left of___

Am   Am⁷   Am

bil - i - ty___ in the fi - re.}   We'll watch the flames grow higher,
all your love___ for the fi - re.}

Asus⁴   Am   Am⁷   Am

but if you get too burnt___   you can't come back home.

28

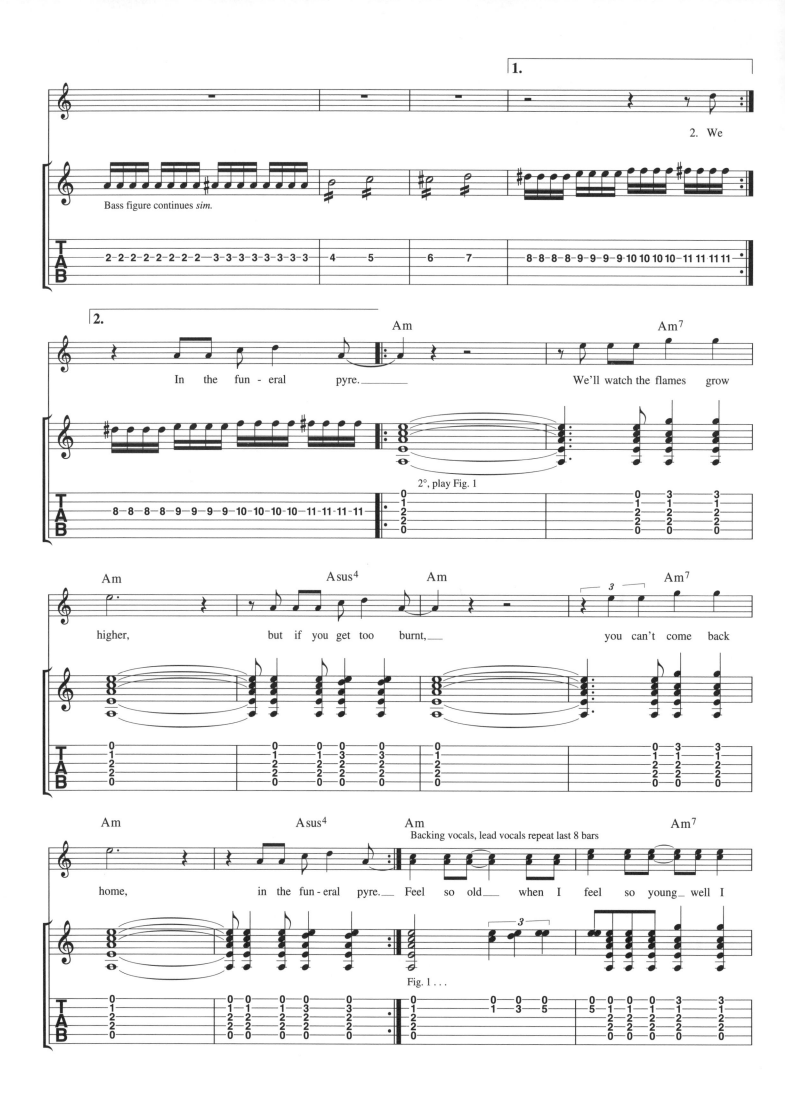

GOING UNDERGROUND

Words & Music by Paul Weller

w/crunch overdrive

Verse

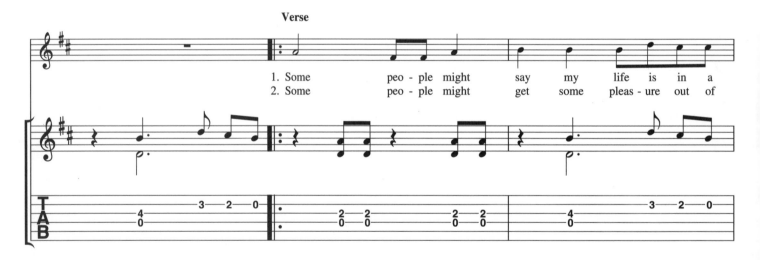

1. Some peo-ple might say my life is in a
2. Some peo-ple might get some pleas-ure out of

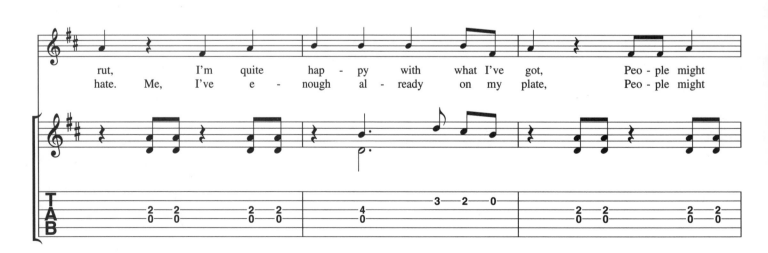

rut, I'm quite hap-py with what I've got, Peo-ple might
hate. Me, I've e-nough al-ready on my plate, Peo-ple might

PRECIOUS

Words & Music by Paul Weller

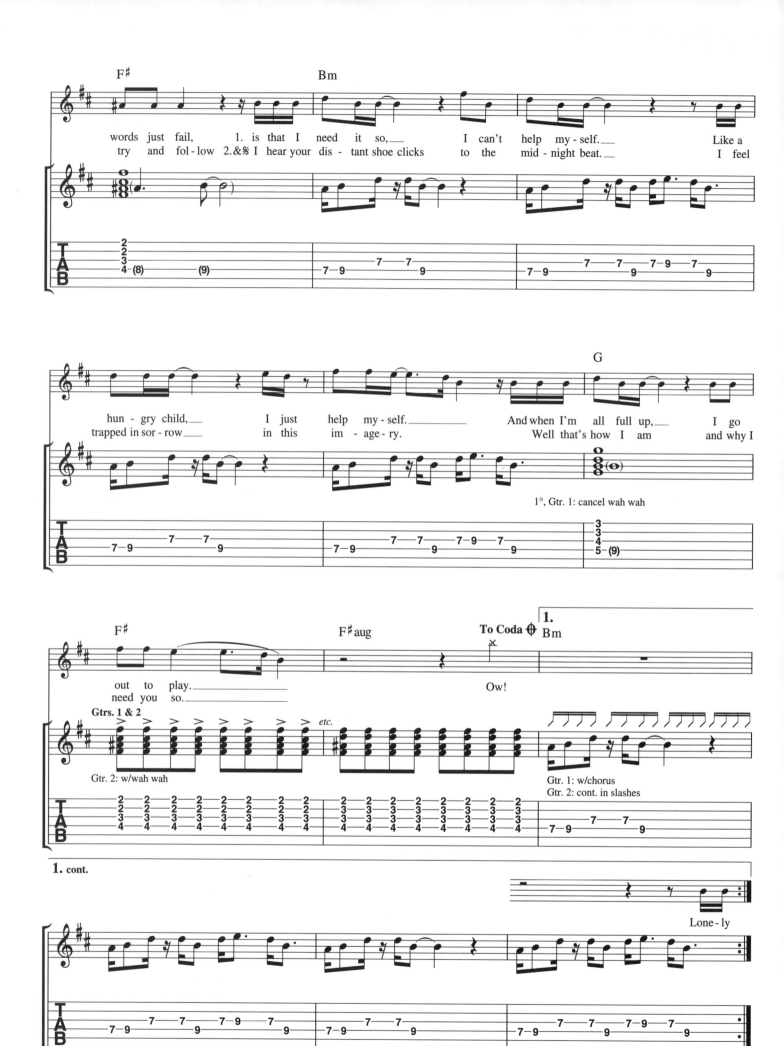

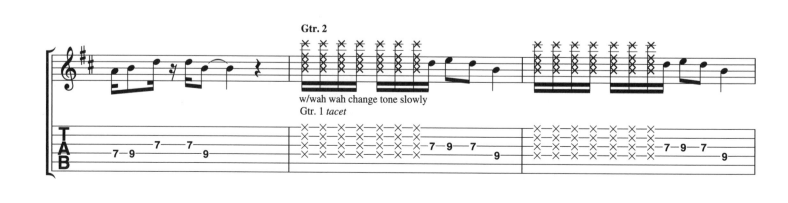

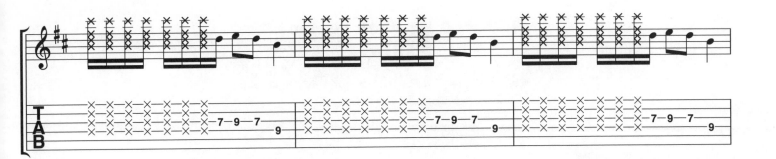

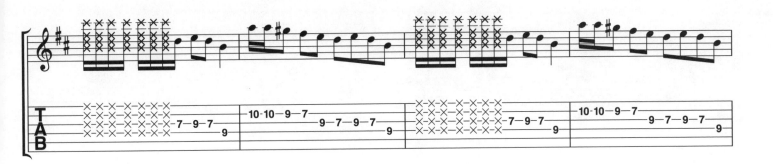

STRANGE TOWN

Words & Music by Paul Weller

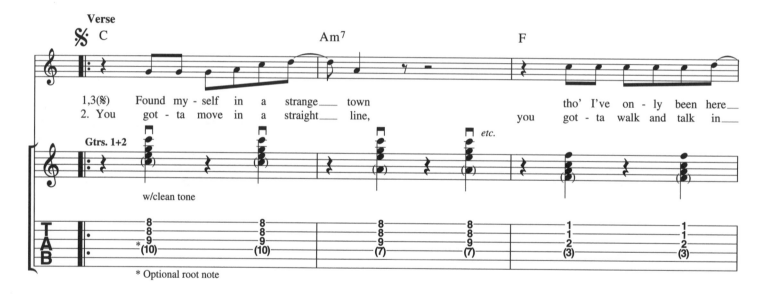

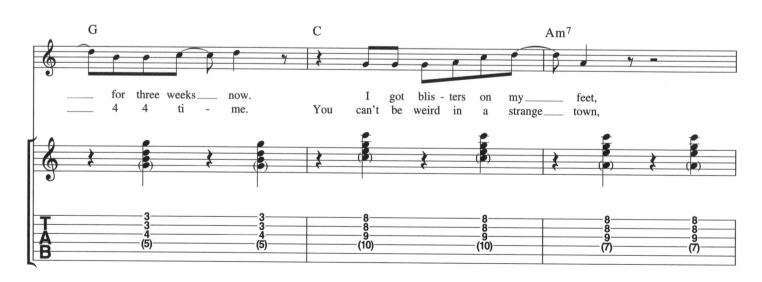

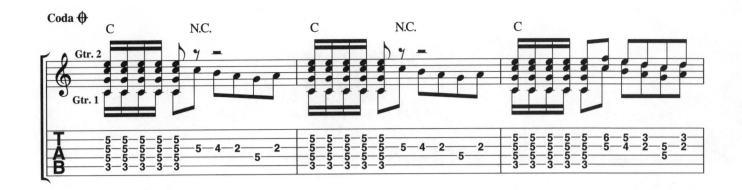

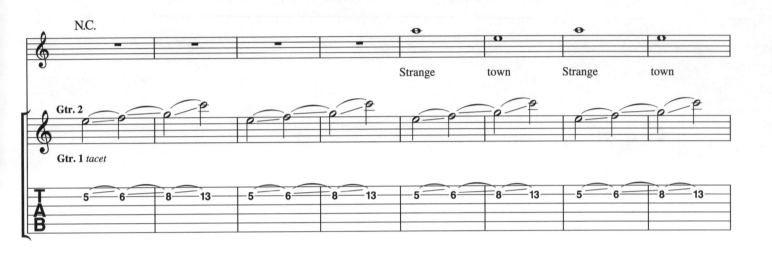

Strange town Strange town

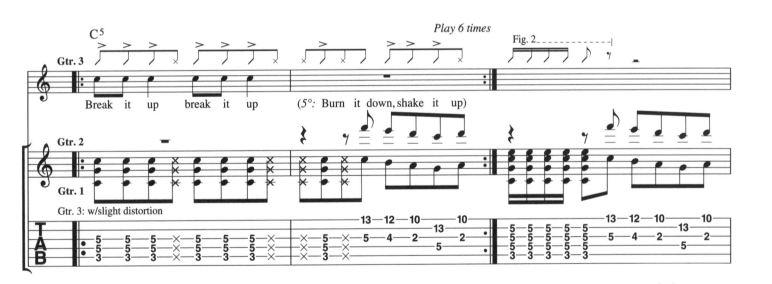

Break it up break it up (5°: Burn it down, shake it up)

Gtr. 3: w/slight distortion

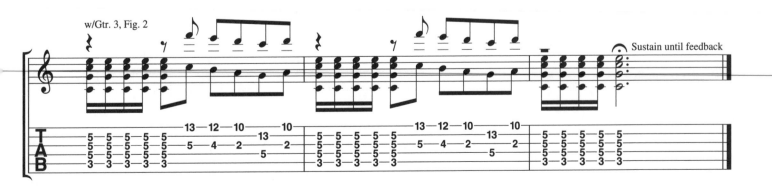

Sustain until feedback

START!

Words & Music by Paul Weller

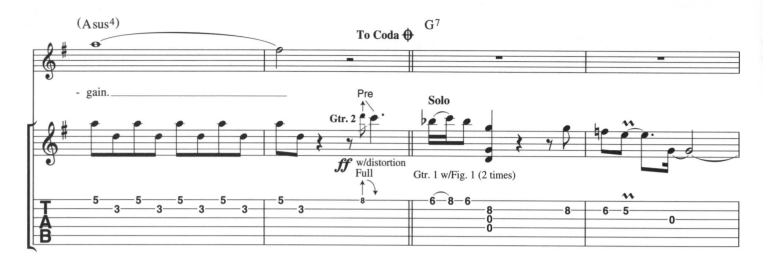

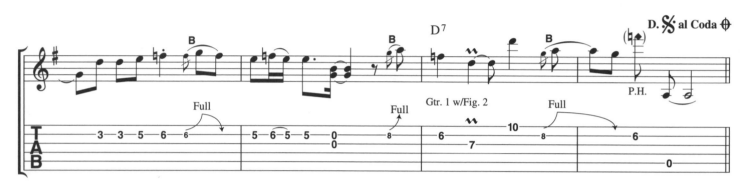

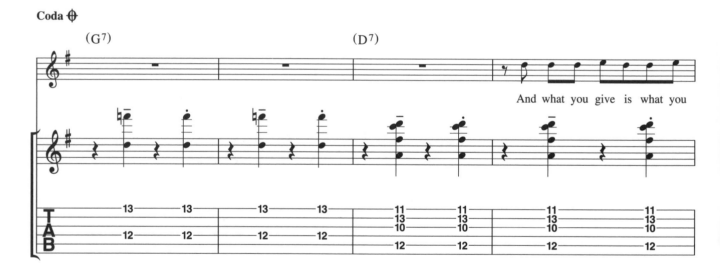

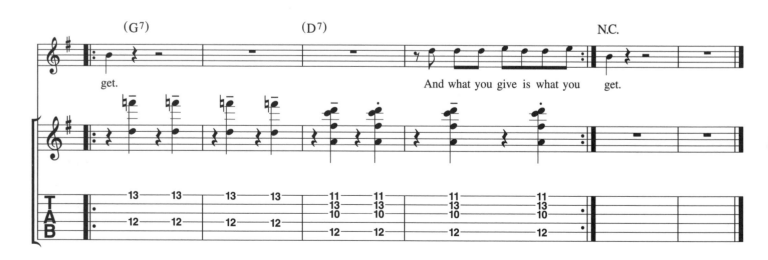

TOWN CALLED MALICE

Words & Music by Paul Weller

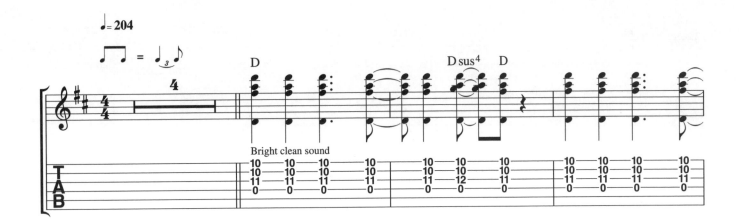

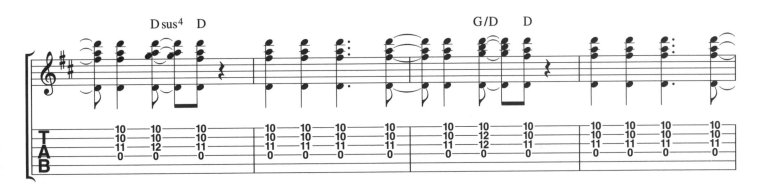

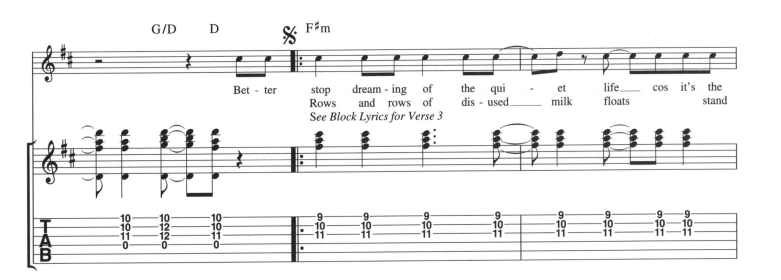

Bet - ter stop dream - ing of the qui - et life___ cos it's the
Rows and rows of dis - used___ milk floats stand
See Block Lyrics for Verse 3

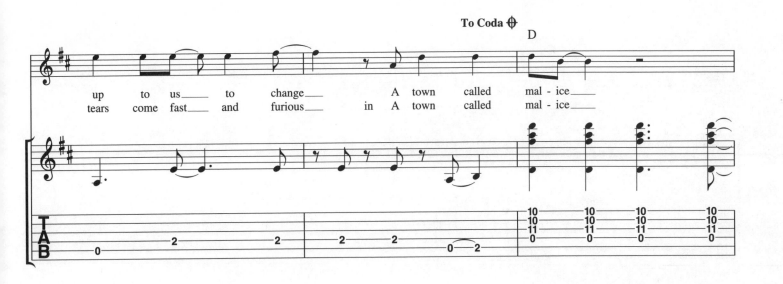

up to us___ to change___ A town called mal - ice___
tears come fast___ and furious___ in A town called mal - ice___

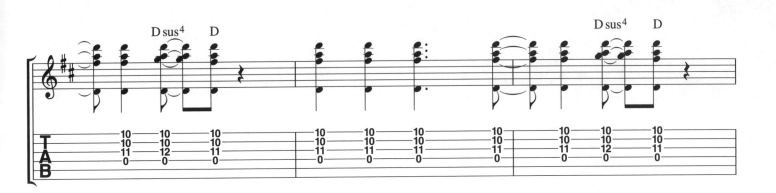

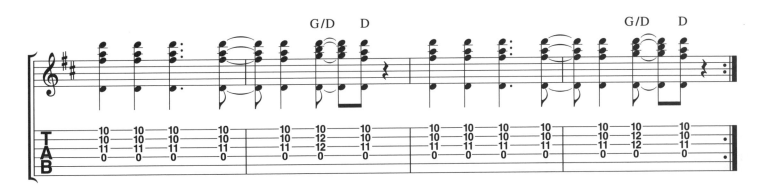

Ba ba ba ba ba da ba.___ Ba ba ba da ba___

Lyrics visible in the music:

A

To eith-er cut down on beer or the kids new gear, it's a big de-cis-ion in a

D

town called mal-ice._____

Dsus⁴ D

Oh   oh

Dsus⁴ D

yeah._____

Finger clicks

D. 𝄋 al Coda ⊕

Ooh - oo_____

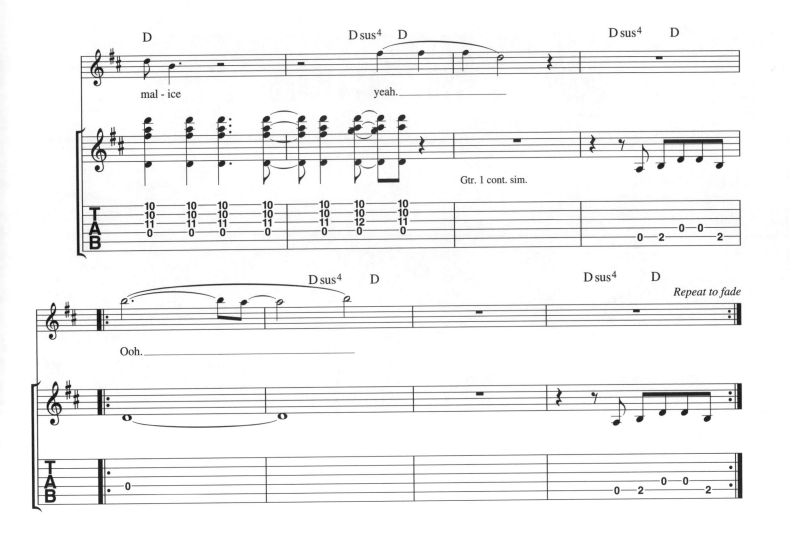

Verse 3:

The ghost of a steam train
Echoes down my track
It's at the moment bound for nowhere
Just going round and round
Playground kids and creaking swings
Lost laughter in the breeze
I could go on for hours
And I probably will
But I'd sooner put some joy back
In this town called Malice.

THAT'S ENTERTAINMENT

Words & Music by Paul Weller

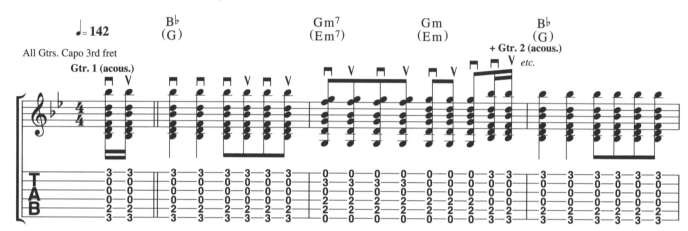

* Symbols in parentheses represent chord names with respect to capoed gtrs.

Tab 0 = 3rd fret. Symbols above reflect actual sounding chords.

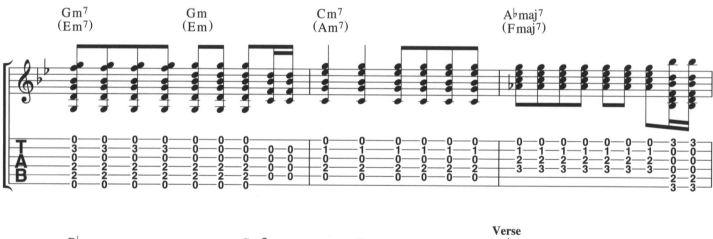

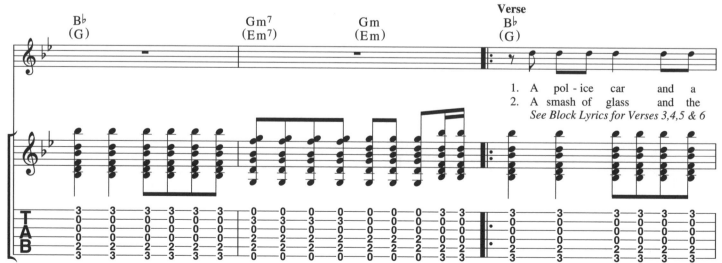

1. A pol - ice car   and a
2. A smash of glass   and the
See Block Lyrics for Verses 3,4,5 & 6

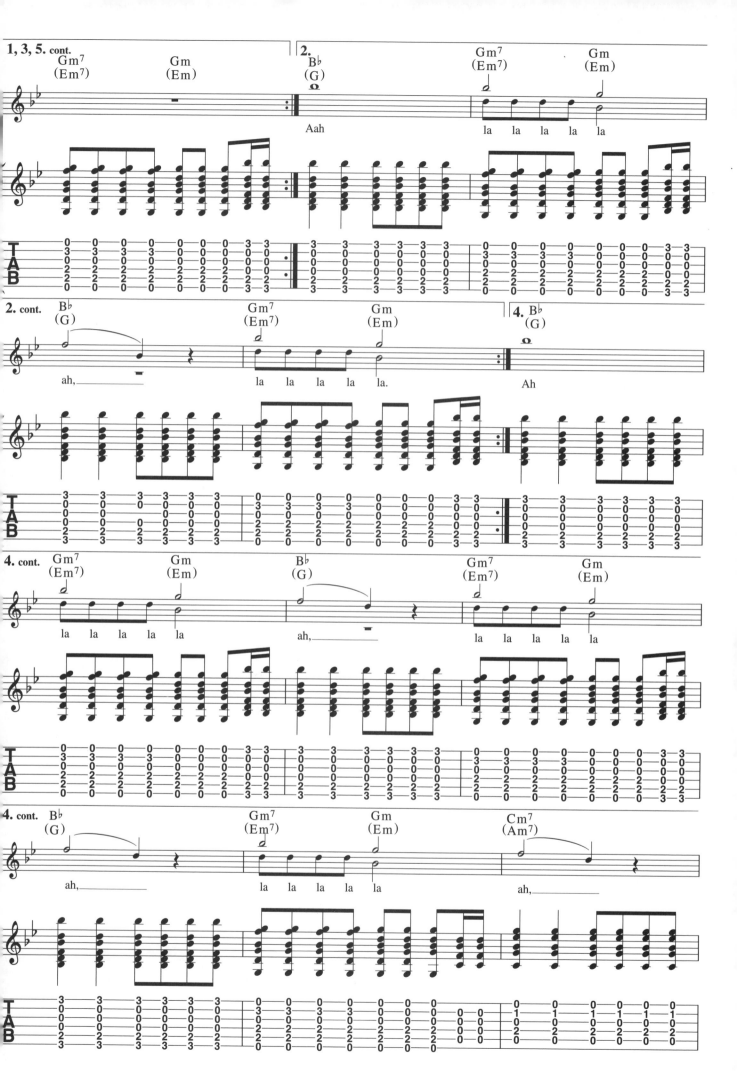

11/98 (32578)

Verse 3: Days of speed and slow time Mondays
Pissing down with rain on a boring Wednesday
Watching the news and not eating your tea
A freezing cold flat and damp on the walls, I say:

Verse 4: Waking up at 6 a.m. on a cool warm morning
Opening the windows and breathing in petrol
An amateur band rehearsing in a nearby yard
Watching the telly and thinking about your holidays.

Verse 5: Waking up from bad dreams and smoking cigarettes
Cuddling a warm girl and smelling stale perfume
A hot summer's day and sticky black tarmac
Feeding ducks in the park and wishing you were far

Verse 6: Two lovers kissing amongst the scream of midnight
Two lovers missing the tranquility of solitude
Getting a cab and travelling on buses
Reading the grafitti about slashed seat affairs.

y Peter Evans
rthur Dick
ged by Dave Holmes
essed by Seton Music Graphics

n by Pearce Marchbank,
nty, London

ographs by Martin Goddard
eatures International

he United Kingdom by
Limited, Thetford, Norfolk